Better Bass With
Rockschool

Welcome To Bass Grade 8

Welcome to the Rockschool Bass Grade 8 pack. The book and CD contain everything needed to play bass in this grade. In the book you will find the exam scores in both standard bass notation and TAB. The accompanying CD has full stereo mixes of each tune, backing tracks to play along with for practice, tuning notes and spoken two bar count-ins to each piece. Handy tips on playing the pieces and the marking schemes can be found in the Guru's Guide on page 28. If you have any queries about this or any other Rockschool exam, please call us on **020 8332 6303**, email us at *info@rockschool.co.uk* or visit our website *www.rockschool.co.uk*. Good luck!

Level 3 Requirements for Grades 6, 7 & 8

The nine Rockschool grades are divided into four levels. These levels correspond to the levels of the National Qualifications Framework (NQF). Further details about the NQF can be found at *www.qca.org.uk/NQF*. Details of all Rockschool's accredited qualifications can be found at *www.qca.org.uk/openquals*.

Bass Grade 8 is part of Level 3. This Level is for those of you who are ready to stretch all aspects of your playing at an advanced level of technique and musical expression.

Grade 6: in this grade you are developing the confidence of the advanced player across the range of physical and expressive techniques. You will start experimenting with a range of techniques across a number of musical styles. There is a greater emphasis on personal expression and you will display your own musical personality through ad libbing and soloing.

Grade 7: in this grade you are now confident in your abilities across the range of physical and expressive techniques. You will be experimenting with a range of these techniques across a number of styles. You will also be comfortable with a range of rhythms and time signatures other than common time. Your solos will be musically expressive and you will have the confidence to apply modal ideas in a number of soloing contexts.

Grade 8: you will play effortlessly with a wide range of physical and expressive techniques at your command. You will be able to use these at will across a range of styles and musical contexts. You will be comfortable playing pieces employing a number of different time signatures (including changes from bar to bar) and you will display mastery of a number of musical styles. Your solos will be highly musical and employ techniques across the range. You will also be highly sensitive to all aspects of musical presentation.

Bass Exams at Grade 8

There are **three** types of exam that can be taken using this pack: a Grade Exam, a Performance Certificate and a Band Exam.

Bass Grade 8 Exam: this is for players who want to develop performance and technical skills

Players wishing to enter for a Bass Grade 8 exam need to prepare **three** pieces of which **one** may be a free choice piece chosen from outside the printed repertoire. In addition you must prepare the technical exercises in the book, undertake a quick study piece, take an ear test and answer general musicianship questions. Samples of these tests are printed in the book along with audio examples on the CD.

Bass Grade 8 Performance Certificate: this is for players who want to focus on performing in a range of styles

To enter for your Bass Grade 8 Performance Certificate you play pieces only. You can choose any **five** of the six tunes printed in this book, or you can choose to bring in up to **two** free choice pieces as long as they meet the standards set out by Rockschool. Free choice piece checklists for all grades can be found on the Rockschool website: *www.rockschool.co.uk*.

Level 3 Band Exam in Guitar, Bass and Drums: this is for players who want to play in a band

The Level 3 band exam is for all of you who would like to play the repertoire at Grade 8 as a three piece band, consisting of guitar, bass and drums. You play together in the exam, using the parts printed in the Grade 8 Guitar, Bass and Drum books. Like the Bass Grade 8 Performance Certificate, you play any **five** of the six printed tunes, or you can include up to **two** free choice pieces as long as they meet the standards set out by Rockschool. If you take this exam you will be marked as a unit with each player expected to contribute equally to the overall performance of each piece played.

Bass Notation Explained

THE MUSICAL STAVE shows pitches and rhythms and is divided by lines into bars. Pitches are named after the first seven letters of the alphabet.

TABLATURE graphically represents the bass guitar fingerboard. Each horizontal line represents a string, and each number represents a fret.

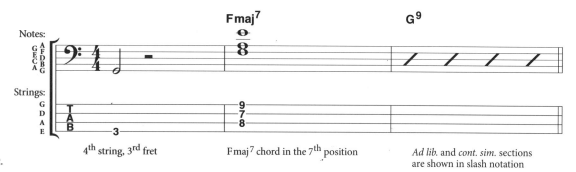

4th string, 3rd fret

Fmaj7 chord in the 7th position

Ad lib. and *cont. sim.* sections are shown in slash notation

Definitions For Special Bass Guitar Notation

HAMMER ON: Pick the lower note, then sound the higher note by fretting it without picking.

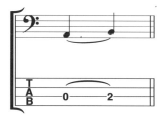

PULL OFF: Pick the higher note then sound the lower note by lifting the finger without picking.

SLIDE: Pick the first note, then slide to the next with the same finger.

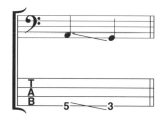

GLISSANDO: Pick the note and slide along the string in the direction indicated.

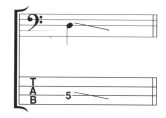

SLAP STYLE: Slap bass technique is indicated through the letters T (thumb) and P (pull).

TAPPING: Sound note by tapping the string – circles denote a picking hand tap, squares a fretting hand tap.

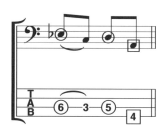

DEAD (GHOST) NOTES: Pick the string while the note is muted with the fretting hand.

NATURAL HARMONICS: Lightly touch the string above the indicated fret then pick to sound a harmonic.

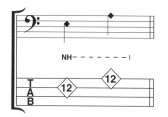

 (accent) • Accentuate note (play it louder).

 (accent) • Accentuate note with great intensity.

 (staccato) • Shorten time value of note.

 • Fermata (Pause)

D.%. al Coda

D.C. al Fine

• Go back to the sign (%), then play until the bar marked ***To Coda*** ⊕ then skip to the section marked ⊕ ***Coda***.

• Go back to the beginning of the song and play until the bar marked ***Fine*** (end).

• Repeat bars between signs.

• When a repeated section has different endings, play the first ending only the first time and the second ending only the second time.

Hussein Boon

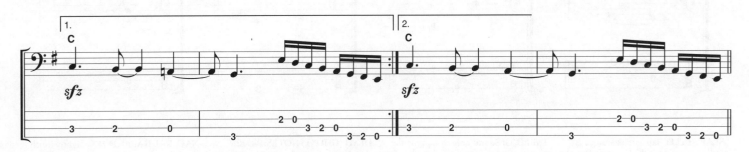

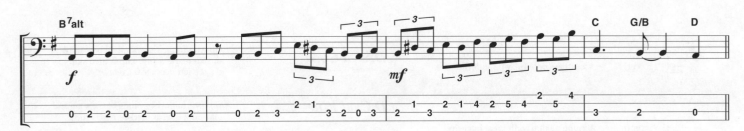

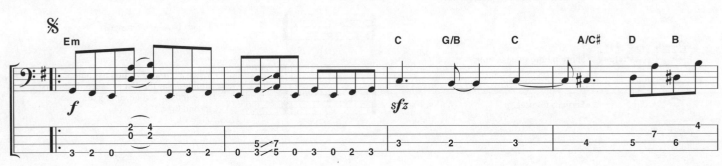

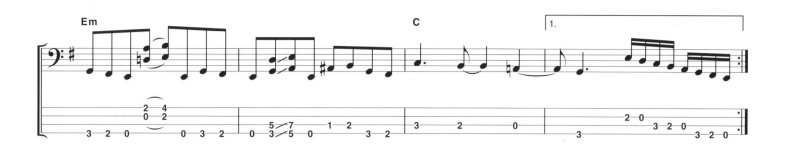

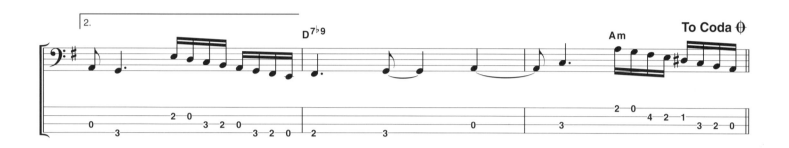

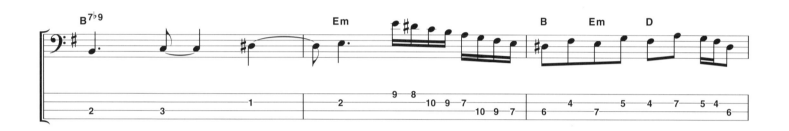

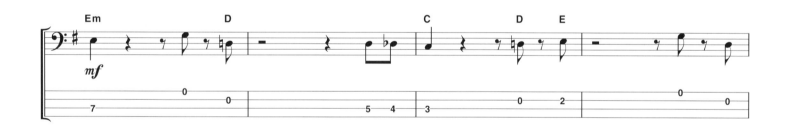

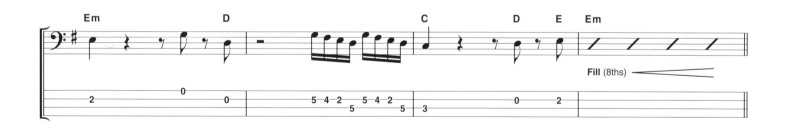

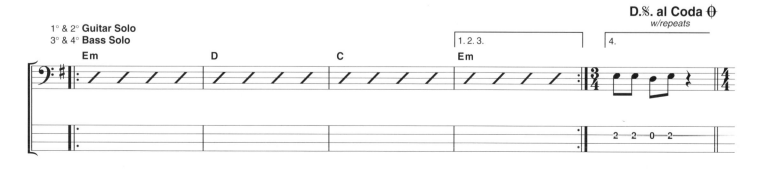

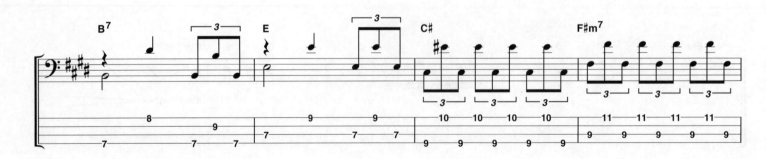

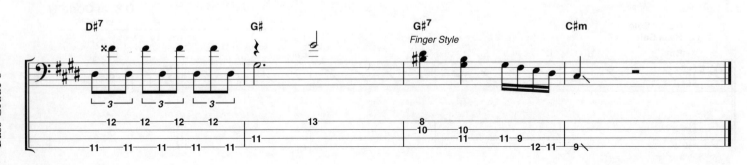

Bonzo

Noam Lederman & James Creed

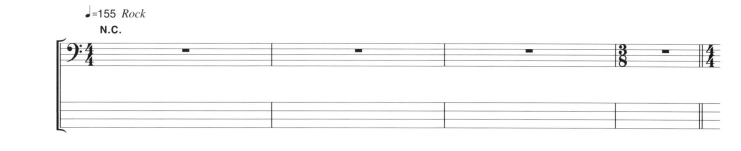

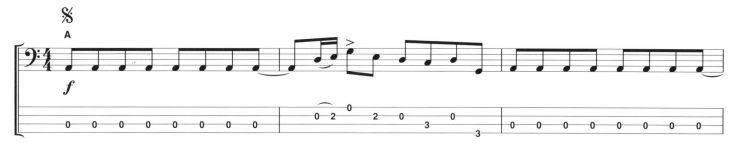

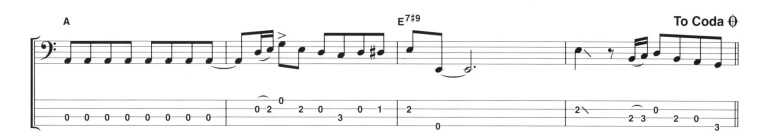

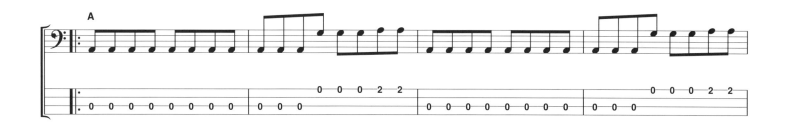

Sampa Samba

Kung Fu Drummer, Kita Steuer & Kiko Perrone

11

Fusion

Jason Woolley

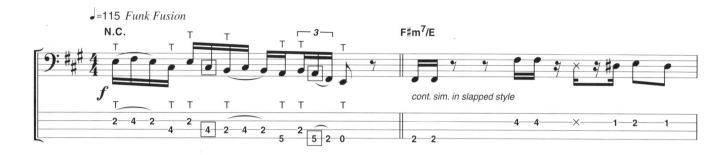

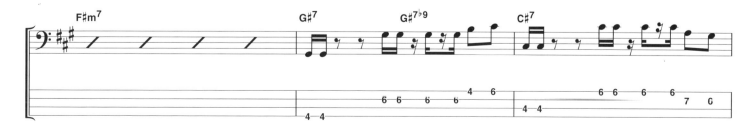

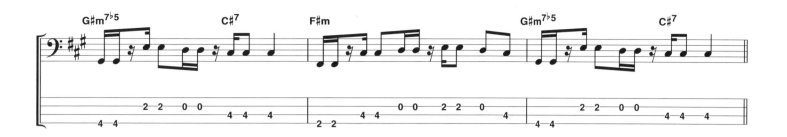

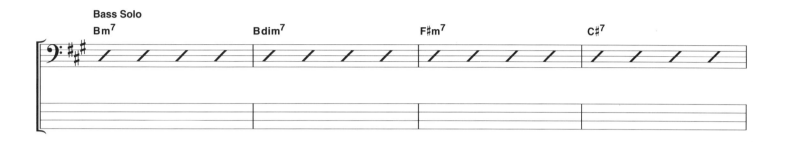

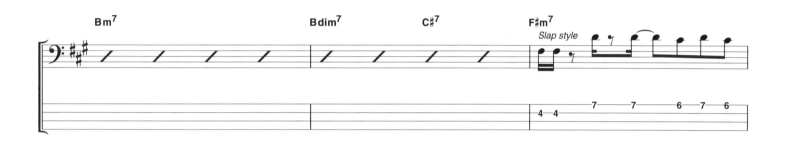

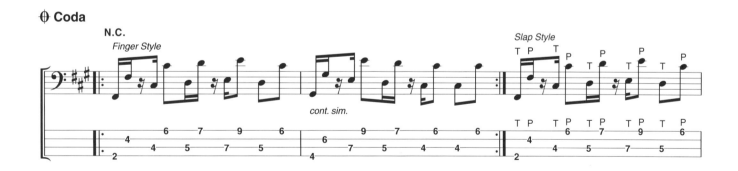

Some You Win

Kit Morgan

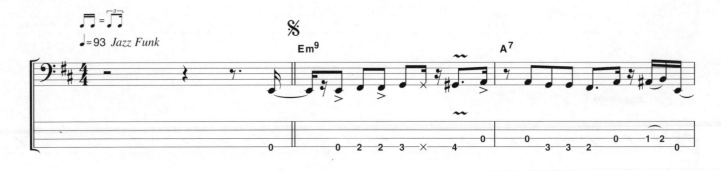

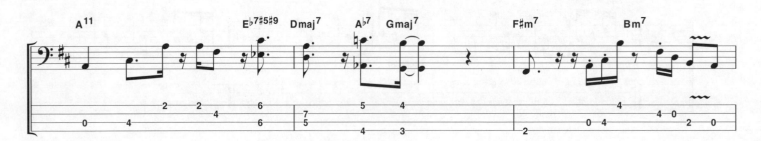

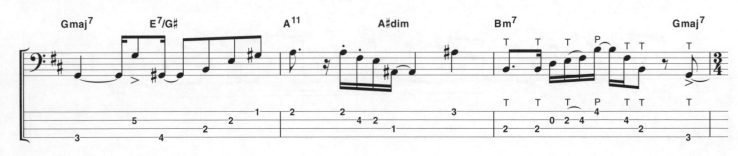

Grade Exam and Performance Certificate Entry Form

Please complete the form below in BLOCK CAPITALS. Information given below will only be used by Rockschool for exam purposes and for Rockschool news. Completed application forms should be sent, along with a cheque made payable to **Rockschool Ltd** for the appropriate fees, to:

Exam Entries, Rockschool, 245 Sandycombe Road, Kew, Richmond, Surrey, TW9 2EW

---

1. Candidate's Details

Full Name (as it will appear on the certificate):

Date of Birth (DD/MM/YY)*:   Gender (M/F)*:   *This information is compulsory but will be used for statistical purposes only

Address:

                                    Postcode:

Telephone No: Mobile No:

Email address:

☐ (Please tick) **Yes!** I would like to receive all correspondence from Rockschool via email (with the exception of certificates and mark sheets which will be posted). *Rockschool will NOT circulate your email address to any third parties.*

---

2. Your Examination

Type of Exam (Grade or Performance Certificate):   Grade:

Instrument: *If you are applying for multiple examinations, please continue below:*

Type of Exam:	Instrument:	Grade:
Type of Exam:	Instrument:	Grade:

Period (A/B/C)*:   *Refer to our website for exam periods and closing dates*

Preferred Town for Examination (*Refer to our website for a list of current towns with Rockschool examination centres*):

Rockschool will endeavour to place you at your preferred town, but cannot guarantee this

Please state any dates that are IMPOSSIBLE for you to attend*:

It is not guaranteed that we can avoid these dates

---

3. Additional information

Drum Candidates. Do you require a left-handed kit?

Will you be bringing your own kit (Grades 6,7,8 only)?   If 'no' Rockschool will provide a drum kit.

Popular Piano Candidates. Will you be bringing your own keyboard?

If 'no', Rockschool can provide either a keyboard or a piano. Please indicate which you prefer :

Special Needs Candidates. Please include a supporting letter with your application explaining your requirements.

All Candidates. If there is any additional information you consider relevant, please attach a note to your application.

---

4. Fees – *For current exam prices please refer to our website, www.rockschool.co.uk or call us on 020 8332 6303*

Fee enclosed:

Cheque Number: PLEASE WRITE CANDIDATE NAME ON BACK OF CHEQUE

Teacher's Exam Entry Form

Teachers wishing to enter **grade exams** and **performance certificates** on behalf of their students should complete the form below in BLOCK CAPITALS. Information given will only be used by Rockschool for exam purposes and for Rockschool news. You can get up to date information on examination prices from **www.rockschool.co.uk** or by ringing the Rockschool helpline on **020 8332 6303**. Completed application forms should be sent, along with a cheque made payable to **Rockschool Ltd** for the appropriate fees, to:

Exam Entries, Rockschool, 245 Sandycombe Road, Kew, Richmond, Surrey, TW9 2EW

---

1. Teacher's Details

Title (Mr/Mrs/Ms etc):   Full Name:

Address:

                                                                   Postcode:

Telephone No: Mobile No:

Email address:

☐ (Please tick) **Yes!** I would like to receive all correspondence from Rockschool via email (with the exception of certificates and mark sheets which will be posted). *Rockschool will NOT circulate your email address to any third parties.*

---

2. Examination Details and Fees
For grade exams, please write 'G' and the grade number in the Grade box (e.g. G6 for Grade 6). For performance certificates, please write 'PC' and the grade number in the Grade box (e.g. PC4 for Performance Certificate Grade 4). †*For examination periods refer to our website. Continue on separate sheet if necessary.*
FOR SPECIAL NEEDS CANDIDATES PLEASE ATTACH A SUPPORTING LETTER WITH DETAILS.

Candidate's Name (as it will appear on the certificate)	Date of Birth	Gender (M/F)	Instrument	Grade*	Period†	Fee (£)
1.	DD MM YYYY					
2.	DD MM YYYY					
3.	DD MM YYYY					
4.	DD MM YYYY					
5.	DD MM YYYY					
6.	DD MM YYYY					
7.	DD MM YYYY					
8.	DD MM YYYY					
9.	DD MM YYYY					
10.	DD MM YYYY					
11.	DD MM YYYY					
12.	DD MM YYYY					
				Total fees enclosed £		

Preferred Town for Examination (*Refer to our website for a list of current towns with Rockschool examination centres**):

*Rockschool will endeavour to place your candidates at your preferred town, but cannot guarantee this

Please list dates your candidate(s) **cannot** attend*:

*It is not guaranteed that we can avoid these dates

Band Exam Entry Form

You can enter for one of the following band exams (1 Guitar player, 1 Bass player, 1 Drummer) using Rockschool materials: *Level One (Grade 3 repertoire)* *Level Two (Grade 5 repertoire)* *Level Three (Grade 8 repertoire)* Please complete the form below in BLOCK CAPITALS. Information given will only be used by Rockschool for exam purposes and for Rockschool news. Completed application forms should be sent, along with a cheque made payable to **Rockschool Ltd** for the appropriate fees, to:

Exam Entries, Rockschool, 245 Sandycombe Road, Kew, Richmond, Surrey, TW9 2EW

1. Band's Details

GUITARIST Full Name (as it will appear on the certificate):

Date of Birth (DD/MM/YY)*:   Gender (M/F)*:

BASSIST Full Name (as it will appear on the certificate):

Date of Birth (DD/MM/YY)*:   Gender (M/F)*:

DRUMMER Full Name (as it will appear on the certificate):

Date of Birth (DD/MM/YY)*:   Gender (M/F)*:

*This information is compulsory but will be used for statistical purposes only

2. Band's Main Contact Details

Main Contact's Name:

Address:

Postcode:

Telephone No: Mobile No:

Email address:

☐ (Please tick) **Yes!** I would like to receive all correspondence from Rockschool via email (with the exception of certificates and mark sheets which will be posted). *Rockschool will NOT circulate your email address to any third parties.*

3. Your Examination — *If you are applying for multiple exams, please use a separate form for each*

Exam Level (One/Two/Three):

Period (A/B/C)*:   *Refer to our website for exam periods and closing dates*

Preferred Town for Examination (*Refer to our website for a list of current towns with Rockschool examination centres*):

Rockschool will endeavour to place you at your preferred town, but cannot guarantee this

Please state any dates that are IMPOSSIBLE for you to attend*:

It is not guaranteed that we can avoid these dates

Additional Information *If there is any additional information you consider relevant (e.g. band members with special needs) please attach a separate sheet explaining your requirements.*

4. Fees — *For current exam prices please refer to our website, www.rockschool.co.uk or call us on 020 8332 6303*

Fee enclosed:

Cheque Number: PLEASE WRITE CANDIDATES' NAMES ON BACK OF CHEQUE

ROCKSCHOOL HELPLINE: 020 8332 6303
email: info@rockschool.co.uk   website: www.rockschool.co.uk

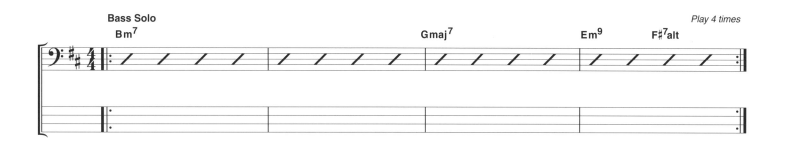

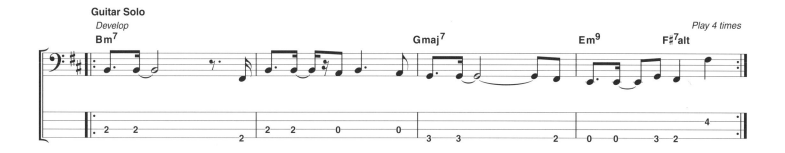

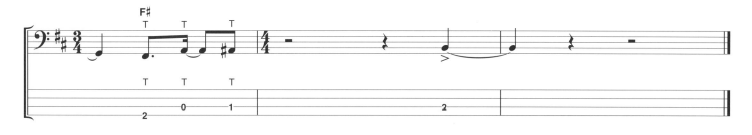

Whatever Happened To Jazz?

Deirdre Cartwright

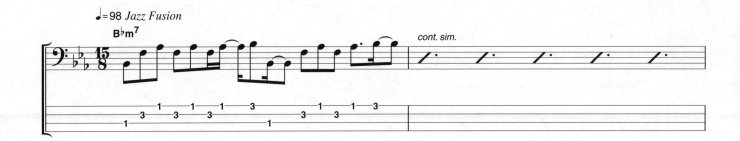

Technical Exercises

In this section, the examiner will ask you to play a selection of exercises drawn from each of the three groups shown below. Groups A and B contain examples of the kinds of scales and arpeggios you can use when playing the pieces. In Group C you will be asked to prepare the exercise and play it to the backing track on the CD. You do not need to memorise the exercises (and can use the book in the exam) but the examiner will be looking for the speed of your response. The examiner will also give credit for the level of your musicality.

Groups A and B should be prepared in all of the following keys: C to E♭ inclusive, and should be played at ♩ = 140. The examiner will give you this tempo in the exam.

Group A: Scales & Modes

1. Two octave major scales. C major scale shown

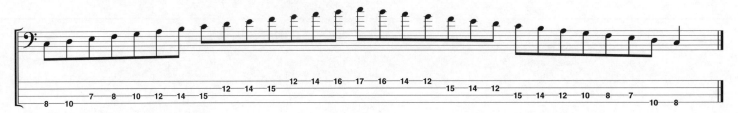

2. Two octave dorian mode. D dorian scale shown

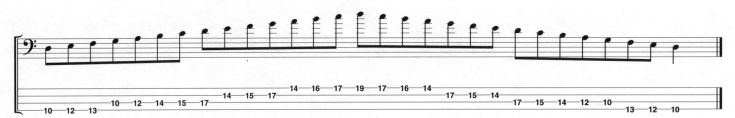

3. Superlocrian (altered) scale. C superlocrian shown

4. Diminished (half tone/whole tone) scales. C diminished scale shown

Group B: Arpeggios

1. Major arpeggio inversions. C major arpeggio inversion shown

2. Minor arpeggio inversions. C minor arpeggio inversion shown

Group C: Harmonics Study

Prepare the following exercise to the CD backing track. You will perform this exercise in the exam to the backing track on the CD.

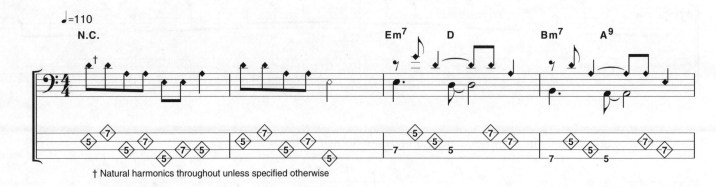

† Natural harmonics throughout unless specified otherwise

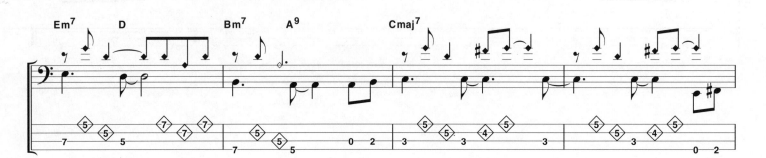

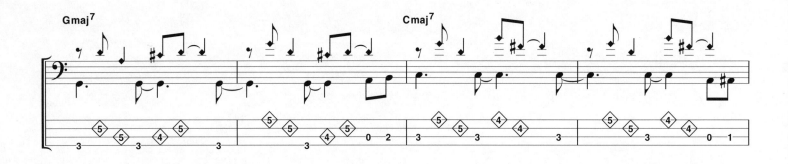

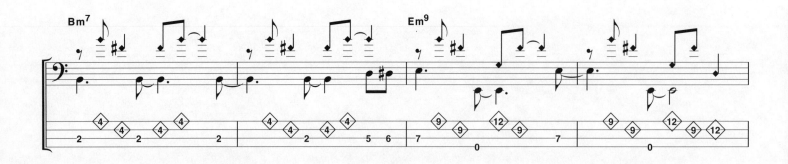

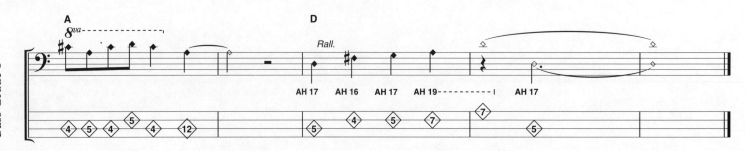

Quick Study Piece

At this grade you will be asked to prepare a short Quick Study Piece (QSP) which will be given for you to prepare with audio 20 minutes before entering the exam room. You should be prepared to play a QSP in any of the following styles: blues, rock, funk or jazz. The QSP is in the form of a lead sheet and it is up to you to create your own interpretation of the music, particularly where you have to compose and perform your own part. You will then perform the piece to a backing track in the exam.

The QSP will be in standard notation and TAB and you are required to master your version of the piece within the time given. Printed below is an example of the type of QSP you are likely to receive in the exam. The CD contains an idealised version and a backing track.

Ear Tests

There are two ear tests in this grade. The examiner will play each test to you on CD. You will find one example of each type of test you will be given in the exam printed below.

Test 1: Melodic Recall

You will be asked to play back on your bass the bass line of a four bar extract scored for guitar, bass and drums composed from C–E♭ major or minor or C–E♭ major or minor pentatonic scales. You will be given the tonic note and you will hear the test twice. There will be a short break for you to practise the test and then the test will recommence. You will play the bassline with the guitar and drum backing. This test is continuous. The tempo is ♩=75.

Test 2: Harmonic Recognition

You will be asked to play the root notes and identify the chord types from the following harmonic progression. You will be told the tonic and hear the progression twice. The tempo is ♩=90.

General Musicianship Questions

You will be asked five General Musicianship Questions at the end of the exam. The examiner will ask questions based on a pieces or pieces you have played in the exam. Some of the theoretical topics can be found in the Technical Exercises.

Topics:

i)   Music theory
ii)   Knowledge of your instrument
iii) History and styles

The music theory questions will cover the following topics at this grade:

Any and all music signs as displayed on the staff
Knowledge of the construction of the following scales:

Dorian & superlocrian modes
Diminished scale

Knowledge of the construction of the following arpeggios:

Major and inversions
Minor and inversions

Knowledge of harmonics

The instrument knowledge questions will cover the following topics at this grade:

All aspects of bass construction
Recognition of main bass makes
Recognition of main bass amplifiers
Use of appropriate tone and volume controls for different styles

The history and styles questions will cover the following topics:

Instrument types associated with famous players
Styles associated with famous players
History of style development
Impact of famous players on playing styles

Questions on all these topics will be based on pieces played by you in the exam. Tips on how to approach this part of the exams can be found in the Rockschool Companion Guide and on the Rockschool website: *www.rockschool.co.uk*

The Guru's Guide To Bass Grade 8

This section contains some handy hints compiled by Rockschool's Bass Guru to help you get the most out of the performance pieces. Do feel free to adapt the tunes to suit your playing style. Remember, these tunes are your chance to show your musical imagination and personality.

The TAB fingerings are suggestions only. Feel free to use different neck positions as they suit you. Please also note that any solos featured in the full mixes are not meant to be indicative of the standard required for the grade.

Bass Grade 8 Tunes

Rockschool tunes help you play the hit tunes you enjoy. The pieces have been written by top pop and rock composers and players according to style specifications drawn up by Rockschool.

The tunes printed here fall into two categories. The first category can be called the 'contemporary mainstream' and features current styles in today's charts. The second category of pieces consists of 'roots styles', those classic grooves and genres which influence every generation of performers.

CD full mix track 1, backing track 8: 667

A thundering heavy rock track that features some of the 'new classical' playing ideas of performers such as Yngwie Malmsteen. The bass part largely follows the guitar line, either by doubling up (eg in the sixteenth note runs at the end of the 1st and 2nd time bars), or by playing parallel lines. However, the bass should not hide behind the guitar line but should rather add to it. The solo section gives scope to show off your rock chops while in the rather baroque sounding outro you can craft your own accompaniment to the guitar.

Composer: Hussein Boon.

CD full mix track 2, backing track 9: Bonzo

The bassline in this Led Zeppelin inspired track consists mainly of syncopated eighth pedal notes, but should be played with plenty of expressive variations and colour. The second half of the piece is largely a matter for your own creative instincts, whether in the bass solo or by supplying accompaniment to the other solos that are present in the song. Dynamic shaping will be important here and you should use this as an expressive tool as much as you can.

Composers: Noam Lederman & James Creed.

CD full mix track 3, backing track 10: Sampa Samba

The bassline in this Latin piece is challenging to say the least and in the first section is shown as played on two staves. The technique here is to hammer on the top two notes (shown in the treble clef) with two fingers of your picking hand, while tapping the notes shown on the bass clef with one finger of your fretting hand. Care also needs to be taken when doing the latter that you damp the top two strings to prevent unwanted noise. The second half of the piece is a more orthodox syncopated thumb and pull funk groove.

Composers: Kung Fu Drummer, Kita Steuer & Kiko Perrone.

CD full mix track 4, backing track 11: Fusion

This is a tightly played funk tune with a tricky opening riff that's played with both the thumb and a fretting hand tap. The main groove is played in varying positions around the fretboard and can be varied with sixteenth note fills and other techniques as you see fit. The groove in the second half is a rhythmic variation of the first, played partly with the fingers and partly with the thumb. The coda is more orthodox thumb and pull octaves but is also rhythmically challenging.

Composer: Jason Woolley.

CD full mix track 5, backing track 12: Some You Win

The key to this jazz funk piece is feel. The groove should bubble underneath the guitar part, providing rhythmic momentum and musical colour. The line should be shaped throughout with accents, dynamic variations, palm muting and staccato. The solo section gives you scope to develop the lines further.

Composer: Kit Morgan.

CD full mix track 6, backing track 13: Whatever Happened To Jazz?

The bass part in this song, played in an array of compound time signatures, is very sparsely written, giving you the opportunity to develop the rolling bassline that sits under the guitar part. Similarly in the guitar solo section you can develop the walking bass part, remembering to shape with dynamic variations and other expressive devices.

Composer: Deirdre Cartwright.

CD Musicians:

Guitars: Deirdre Cartwright; John Parricelli; Hussein Boon; Keith Airey
Bass: Henry Thomas
Drums: Noam Lederman
Keyboards and programming: Alastair Gavin

Bass Grade 8 Marking Schemes

The table below shows the marking scheme for the Bass Grade 8 exam.

ELEMENT	PASS	MERIT	DISTINCTION
Piece 1	13 out of 20	15 out of 20	17+ out of 20
Piece 2	13 out of 20	15 out of 20	17+ out of 20
Piece 3	13 out of 20	15 out of 20	17+ out of 20
Technical Exercises	6 out of 10	7–8 out of 10	9+ out of 10
Quick Study Piece	11 out of 15	12–13 out of 15	14+ out of 15
Ear Tests	6 out of 10	7–8 out of 10	9+ out of 10
General Musicianship Questions	3 out of 5	4 out of 5	5 out of 5
Total Marks	**Pass: 65%+**	**Merit: 75%+**	**Distinction: 85%+**

The table below shows the markings scheme for the Bass Grade 8 Performance Certificate and the Level 3 Band Exam.

ELEMENT	PASS	MERIT	DISTINCTION
Piece 1	14 out of 20	16 out of 20	18+ out of 20
Piece 2	14 out of 20	16 out of 20	18+ out of 20
Piece 3	14 out of 20	16 out of 20	18+ out of 20
Piece 4	14 out of 20	16 out of 20	18+ out of 20
Piece 5	14 out of 20	16 out of 20	18+ out of 20
Total Marks	**Pass: 70%+**	**Merit: 80%+**	**Distinction: 90%+**

Entering Rockschool Exams

Entering a Rockschool exam is easy. Please read through these instructions carefully before filling in the exam entry form. Information on current exam fees can be obtained from Rockschool by ringing 020 8332 6303 or by logging on to our website *www.rockschool.co.uk*.

- You should enter for your exam when you feel ready.

- You can enter for any one of three examination periods. These are shown below with their closing dates.

PERIOD	DURATION	CLOSING DATE
Period A	1st February to 15th March	1st December
Period B	1st May to 31st July	1st April
Period C	23rd October to 15th December	1st October

These dates will apply from 1st September 2006 until further notice

- Please complete the form giving the information required. Please fill in the type and level of exam, the instrument, along with the period and year. Finally, fill in the fee box with the appropriate amount. You can obtain up to date information on all Rockschool exam fees from the website: *www.rockschool.co.uk*. You should send this form with a cheque or postal order (payable to Rockschool Ltd) to the address shown on the order form. **Please also indicate on the form whether or not you would like to receive notification via email.**

- Applications received after the expiry of the closing date may be accepted subject to the payment of an additional fee.

- When you enter an exam you will receive from Rockschool an acknowledgement letter or email containing a copy of our exam regulations.

- Rockschool will allocate your entry to a centre and you will receive notification of the exam, showing a date, location and time as well as advice of what to bring to the centre. We endeavour to give you four weeks' notice of your exam.

- You should inform Rockschool of any cancellations or alterations to the schedule as soon as you can as it is usually not possible to transfer entries from one centre, or one period, to another without the payment of an additional fee.

- Please bring your music book and CD to the exam. You may not use photocopied music, nor the music used by someone else in another exam. The examiner will sign each book during each examination. You may be barred from taking an exam if you use someone else's music.

- You should aim to arrive for your Grade 8 exam thirty minutes before the time stated on the schedule.

- Each Grade 8 exam is scheduled to last for 30 minutes. You can use a small proportion of this time to tune up and get ready.

- Two to three weeks after the exam you will receive a copy of the examiner's mark sheet. Every successful player will receive a Rockschool certificate of achievement.